The Complete Plant Based Diet Recipe Book For Beginners

The Ultimate Beginners Detailed Plant-Based Recipe Book for Losing Weight and Increase your Life Energy

Valerie Harvey

Table of Contents

Introduction

A plant-based diet is a diet based primarily on whole plant foods. It is identical to the regular diet we're used to already, except that it leaves out foods that are not exclusively from plants. Hence, a plant-based diet does away with all types of animal-sourced foods, hydrogenated oils, refined sugars, and processed foods. A whole food plant-based diet comprises not just fruits and vegetables; it also consists of unprocessed or barely-processed oils with healthy monounsaturated fats (like extra-virgin olive oil), whole grains, legumes (essentially lentils and beans), seeds and nuts, as well as herbs and spices. What makes a plant-based meal (or any meal) fun is the manner with which you make them; the seasoning process; and the combination process that contributes to a fantastic flavor and makes every meal unique and enjoyable. There are lots of delicious recipes (all plant-centered), which will prove helpful in when you intend making mouthwatering, healthy plant-based dishes for personal or household consumption. Provided you're eating these plant-based foods regularly, you'll have very problems with fat or diseases that result from bad dietary habits, and there would be no need for excessive calorie tracking. Plant-based diet recipes are versatile; they range from colorful Salads to Lentil Stews, and Bean Burritos. The recipes also draw influences from around the globe, with Mexican, Chinese, European, Indian cuisines all part of the vast array of plant-based recipes available to choose from. Why You Ought to Reduce Your Intake of Processed and Animal-Based Foods. You have likely heard over and over that processed food has adverse effects on your health. You might have also been told repeatedly to stay away from foods with lots of preservatives; nevertheless, nobody ever offered any genuine or concrete facts about why you ought to avoid these foods and why they are unsafe. Consequently, let us properly dissect it to help you properly comprehend why you ought to stay away from these healthy eating offenders. They have massive habit-forming characteristics. Humans have a predisposition towards being addicted to some specific foods; however, the reality is that the fault is not wholly ours. Every one of the unhealthy treats we relish now and then triggers the dopamine release in our brains. This creates a pleasurable effect in our brain, but the excitement is usually short-lived. The discharged dopamine additionally causes an attachment connection gradually, and this is the reason some people consistently go back to eat certain unhealthy foods even when they know it's unhealthy and unnecessary. You can get rid of this by taking out that inducement completely. They are sugar-laden and plenteous in glucose-fructose syrup. Animal-based and processed foods are laden with refined sugars and glucose-fructose syrup which has almost no beneficial food nutrient. An ever-increasing number of studies are affirming what several people presumed from the start; that genetically modified foods bring about inflammatory bowel disease, which consequently makes it increasingly difficult for the body to assimilate essential nutrients. The disadvantages that result from your body being unable to assimilate essential nutrients from consumed foods rightly cannot be overemphasized. Processed and animal-based food products contain plenteous amounts of refined carbohydrates. Indeed, your body requires carbohydrates to give it the needed energy to run body capacities. In any case, refining carbs dispenses with the fundamental supplements; in the way that refining entire grains disposes of the whole grain part. What remains, in the wake of refining, is what's considered as empty carbs or empty calories. These can negatively affect the metabolic system in your body by sharply increasing your blood sugar and insulin quantities. They contain lots of synthetic ingredients. At the point when your body is taking in non-natural ingredients, it regards them as foreign substances. Your body treats them as a health threat. Your body isn't accustomed to identifying synthetic compounds like sucralose or these synthesized sugars. Hence, in defense of your health against this foreign "aggressor," your body does what it's capable of to safeguard your health. It sets off an immune reaction to tackle this "enemy" compound, which indirectly weakens your body's general disease alertness, making you susceptible to illnesses. The concentration and energy expended by your body in ensuring your immune system remain safe could instead be devoted somewhere else. They contain constituent elements that set off an excitable reward sensation in your body. A part of processed and animal-based foods contain compounds like glucose-fructose syrup, monosodium glutamate, and specific food dyes that can trigger some addiction. They rouse your body to receive a benefit in return whenever you consume them. Monosodium glutamate, for example, is added to many store-bought baked foods. This additive slowly conditions your palates to relish the taste. It gets mental just by how your brain interrelates with your taste sensors.

This reward-centric arrangement makes you crave it increasingly, which ends up exposing you to the danger of over consuming calories.

For animal protein, usually, the expression "subpar" is used to allude to plant proteins since they generally have lower levels of essential amino acids as against animal-sourced protein. Nevertheless, what the vast majority don't know is that large amounts of essential amino acids can prove detrimental to your health. Let me break it down further for you.

Strawberry Shake

Preparation Time: 10 minutes

Cooking Time: 10 minutes

Servings: 2

Ingredients:

- 1½ cups fresh strawberries, hulled
- 1 large frozen banana, peeled
- 2 scoops unsweetened vegan vanilla Protein powder
- 2 tablespoons hemp seeds
- 2 cups unsweetened hemp milk

Directions:

In a high-speed blender, place all the ingredients and pulse until creamy.

Pour into two glasses and serve immediately.

Nutrition:

Calories: 259

Fat: 3g

Protein: 10g

Sugar: 2g

Chocolatey Banana Shake

Preparation Time: 10 minutes

Cooking Time: 10 minutes

Servings: 2

Ingredients:

- 2 medium frozen bananas, peeled
- 4 dates, pitted
- 4 tablespoons peanut butter
- 4 tablespoons rolled oats
- 2 tablespoons cacao powder
- 2 tablespoons chia seeds
- 2 cups unsweetened soymilk

Directions:

1. Place all the ingredients in a high-speed blender and pulse until creamy.
2. Pour into two glasses and serve immediately.

Nutrition:

Calories: 502

Fat: 4g

Protein: 11g

Sugar: 9g

Fruity Tofu Smoothie

Preparation Time: 10 minutes

Cooking Time: 10 minutes

Servings: 2

Ingredients:

- 12 ounces silken tofu, pressed and drained
- 2 medium bananas, peeled
- 1½ cups fresh blueberries
- 1 tablespoon maple syrup
- 1½ cups unsweetened soymilk
- ¼ cup ice cubes

Directions:

1. Place all the ingredients in a high-speed blender and pulse until creamy.
2. Pour into two glasses and serve immediately.

Nutrition:

Calories 235

Carbohydrates: 1.9g

Protein: 14.3g

Fat: 18.9g

Green Fruity Smoothie

Preparation Time: 10 minutes

Cooking Time: 10 minutes

Servings: 2

Ingredients:

1 cup frozen mango, peeled, pitted, and chopped

1 large frozen banana, peeled

2 cups fresh baby spinach

1 scoop unsweetened vegan vanilla Protein powder

¼ cup pumpkin seeds

2 tablespoons hemp hearts

1½ cups unsweetened almond milk

Directions:

In a high-speed blender, place all the ingredients and pulse until creamy.

Pour into two glasses and serve immediately.

Nutrition:

Calories 206

Carbohydrates: 1.3g

Protein: 23.5g

Fat: 11.9g

Protein Latte

Preparation Time: 10 minutes

Cooking Time: 10 minutes

Servings: 2

Ingredients:

- 2 cups hot brewed coffee
- 1¼ cups coconut milk
- 2 teaspoons coconut oil
- 2 scoops unsweetened vegan vanilla Protein powder

Directions:

Place all the ingredients in a high-speed blender and pulse until creamy.

Pour into two serving mugs and serve immediately.

Nutrition:

Calories 483

Carbs: 5.2g

Protein: 45.2g

Fat: 31.2g

Health Boosting Juices

Preparation Time: 10 minutes

Cooking Time: 15 minutes

Servings: 2

Ingredients for a red juice:

 4 beetroots, quartered

 2 cups of strawberries

 2 cups of blueberries

Ingredients for an orange juice:

 4 green or red apples, halved

 10 carrots

 ½ lemon, peeled

 1" of ginger

Ingredients for a yellow juice:

 2 green or red apples, quartered

 4 oranges, peeled and halved

 ½ lemon, peeled

 1" of ginger

Ingredients for a lime juice:

 6 stalks of celery

 1 cucumber

 2 green apples, quartered

 2 pears, quartered

Ingredients for a green juice:

½ a pineapple, peeled and sliced

8 leaves of kale

2 fresh bananas, peeled

Directions:

Juice all ingredients in a juicer, chill and serve.

Nutrition:

Calories 316

Carbs: 13.5g

Protein: 37.8g

Fat: 12.2g

Thai Iced Tea

Preparation Time: 5 minutes

Cooking Time: 10 minutes

Servings: 4

Ingredients:

4 cups of water

1 can of light coconut milk (14 oz.)

¼ cup of maple syrup

¼ cup of muscovado sugar

1 teaspoon of vanilla extract

2 tablespoons of loose-leaf black tea

Directions:

In a large saucepan, over medium heat bring the water to a boil.

Turn off the heat and add in the tea, cover and let steep for five minutes.

Strain the tea into a bowl or jug. Add the maple syrup, muscovado sugar, and vanilla extract. Give it a good whisk to blend all the ingredients together.

Set in the refrigerator to chill. Upon serving, pour ¾
of the tea into each glass, top with coconut milk
and stir.

Tips:

Add a shot of dark rum to turn this iced tea into a
cocktail.

You could substitute the coconut milk for almond
or rice milk too.

Nutrition:

Calories 844

Carbohydrates: 2.3g

Protein: 21.6g

Fat: 83.1g

Hot Chocolate

Preparation Time: 5 minutes

Cooking Time: 15 minutes

Servings: 2

Ingredients:

Pinch of brown sugar

2 cups of milk, soy or almond, unsweetened

2 tablespoons of cocoa powder

½ cup of vegan chocolate

Directions:

In a medium saucepan, over medium heat gently bring the milk to a boil. Whisk in the cocoa powder.

Remove from the heat, add a pinch of sugar and chocolate. Give it a good stir until smooth, serve and enjoy.

Tips:

You may substitute the almond or soy milk for coconut milk too.

Nutrition:

Calories 452

Carbs: 29.8g

Protein: 15.2g

Fat: 30.2g

Chai and Chocolate Milkshake

Preparation Time: 5 minutes

Cooking Time: 15 minutes

Servings: 2 servings

Ingredients:

- 1 and ½ cups of almond milk, sweetened or unsweetened
- 3 bananas, peeled and frozen 12 hours before use
- 4 dates, pitted
- 1 and ½ teaspoons of chocolate powder, sweetened or unsweetened
- ½ teaspoon of vanilla extract
- ½ teaspoon of cinnamon
- ¼ teaspoon of ground ginger
- Pinch of ground cardamom
- Pinch of ground cloves
- Pinch of ground nutmeg
- ½ cup of ice cubes

Directions:

Add all the ingredients to a blender except for the ice-cubes. Pulse until smooth and creamy, add the ice-cubes, pulse a few more times and serve.

Tips:

The dates provide enough sweetness to the recipe, however, you are welcome to add maple syrup or honey for a sweeter drink.

Nutrition:

Calories 452

Carbs: 29.8g

Protein: 15.2g

Fat: 30.2g

Colorful Infused Water

Preparation Time: 5 minutes

Cooking Time: 1 hour

Servings: 8 servings

Ingredients:

   1 cup of strawberries, fresh or frozen

   1 cup of blueberries, fresh or frozen

   1 tablespoon of baobab powder

   1 cup of ice cubes

   4 cups of sparkling water

Directions:

   In a large water jug, add in the sparkling water, ice
      cubes, and baobab powder. Give it a good stir.

   Add in the strawberries and blueberries and cover
      the infused water, store in the refrigerator for
      one hour before serving.

Tips:

Store for 12 hours for optimum taste and
nutritional benefits.

Instead of using strawberries and blueberries, add slices of lemon and six mint leaves, one cup of mangoes or cherries, or half a cup of leafy greens such as kale and/or spinach.

Nutrition:

Calories 163

Carbs: 4.1g

Protein: 1.7g

Fat: 15.5g

Hibiscus Tea

Preparation Time: 1 Minute

Cooking Time: 5 minutes

Servings: 2 servings

Ingredients:

1 tablespoon of raisins, diced

6 Almonds, raw and unsalted

½ teaspoon of hibiscus powder

2 cups of water

Directions:

Bring the water to a boil in a small saucepan, add in the hibiscus powder and raisins. Give it a good stir, cover and let simmer for a further two minutes.

Strain into a teapot and serve with a side helping of almonds.

Tips:

As an alternative to this tea, do not strain it and serve with the raisin pieces still swirling around in the teacup.

You could also serve this tea chilled for those hotter days.

Double or triple the recipe to provide you with iced-tea to enjoy during the week without having to make a fresh pot each time.

Nutrition:

Calories 139

Carbohydrates: 2.7g

Protein: 8.7g

Fat: 10.3

Lemon and Rosemary Iced Tea

Preparation Time: 5 minutes

Cooking Time: 10 minutes

Servings: 4 servings

Ingredients:

4 cups of water

4 earl grey tea bags

¼ cup of sugar

2 lemons

1 sprig of rosemary

Directions:

Peel the two lemons and set the fruit aside.

In a medium saucepan, over medium heat combine the water, sugar, and lemon peels. Bring this to a boil.

Remove from the heat and place the rosemary and tea into the mixture. Cover the saucepan and steep for five minutes.

Add the juice of the two peeled lemons to the mixture, strain, chill, and serve.

Tips: Skip the sugar and use honey to taste.

Do not squeeze the tea bags as they can cause the tea to become bitter.

Nutrition:

Calories 229

Carbs: 33.2g

Protein: 31.1g

Fat: 10.2g

Lavender and Mint Iced Tea

Preparation Time: 5 minutes

Cooking Time: 10 minutes

Servings: 8 servings

Ingredients:

8 cups of water

1/3 cup of dried lavender buds

¼ cup of mint

Directions:

Add the mint and lavender to a pot and set this aside.

Add in eight cups of boiling water to the pot. Sweeten to taste, cover and let steep for ten minutes. Strain, chill, and serve.

Tips:

Use a sweetener of your choice when making this iced tea.

Add spirits to turn this iced tea into a summer cocktail.

Nutrition:

Calories 266

Carbs: 9.3g

Protein: 20.9g

Fat: 16.1g

Pear Lemonade

Preparation Time: 5 minutes

Cooking Time: 30 minutes

Servings: 2 servings

Ingredients:

½ cup of pear, peeled and diced

1 cup of freshly squeezed lemon juice

½ cup of chilled water

Directions:

Add all the ingredients into a blender and pulse until
it has all been combined. The pear does make
the lemonade frothy, but this will settle.

Place in the refrigerator to cool and then serve.

Tips:

Keep stored in a sealed container in the
refrigerator for up to four days.

Pop the fresh lemon in the microwave for ten
minutes before juicing, you can extract more juice
if you do this.

Nutrition:

Calories: 160

Carbs: 6.3g

Protein: 2.9g

Fat: 13.6g

Energizing Ginger Detox Tonic

Preparation Time: 15 minutes

Cooking Time: 10 minutes

Servings:

Ingredients:

   1/2 teaspoon of grated ginger, fresh

   1 small lemon slice

   1/8 teaspoon of cayenne pepper

   1/8 teaspoon of ground turmeric

   1/8 teaspoon of ground cinnamon

   1 teaspoon of maple syrup

   1 teaspoon of apple cider vinegar

   2 cups of boiling water

Directions:

   Pour the boiling water into a small saucepan, add
      and stir the ginger, then let it rest for 8 to 10
      minutes, before covering the pan.

   Pass the mixture through a strainer and into the
      liquid, add the cayenne pepper, turmeric,
      cinnamon and stir properly.

   Add the maple syrup, vinegar, and lemon slice.

Add and stir an infused lemon and serve immediately.

Nutrition:

Calories 443

Carbs:9.7 g

Protein: 62.8g

Fat: 16.9g

Warm Spiced Lemon Drink

Preparation Time: 10 minutes

Cooking Time: 2 hours

Servings: 12

Ingredients:

1 cinnamon stick, about 3 inches long

1/2 teaspoon of whole cloves

2 cups of coconut sugar

4 fluid of ounce pineapple juice

1/2 cup and 2 tablespoons of lemon juice

12 fluid ounce of orange juice

2 1/2 quarts of water

Directions:

Pour water into a 6-quarts slow cooker and stir the sugar and lemon juice properly.

Wrap the cinnamon, the whole cloves in cheesecloth and tie its corners with string.

Immerse this cheesecloth bag in the liquid present in the slow cooker and cover it with the lid.

Then plug in the slow cooker and let it cook on high heat setting for 2 hours or until it is heated thoroughly.

When done, discard the cheesecloth bag and serve the drink hot or cold.

Nutrition:

Calories 523

Carbohydrates: 4.6g

Protein: 47.9g

Fat: 34.8g

Soothing Ginger Tea Drink

Preparation Time: 5 minutes

Cooking Time: 2 hours 20 minutes

Servings: 8

Ingredients:

- 1 tablespoon of minced gingerroot
- 2 tablespoons of honey
- 15 green tea bags
- 32 fluid ounce of white grape juice
- 2 quarts of boiling water

Directions:

1. Pour water into a 4-quarts slow cooker, immerse tea bags, cover the cooker and let stand for 10 minutes.
2. After 10 minutes, remove and discard tea bags and stir in remaining ingredients.
3. Return cover to slow cooker, then plug in and let cook at high heat setting for 2 hours or until heated through.
4. When done, strain the liquid and serve hot or cold.

Nutrition:

Calories 232

Carbs: 7.9g

Protein: 15.9g

Fat: 15.1g

Nice Spiced Cherry Cider

Preparation Time: 1 hour 5 minutes

Cooking Time: 3 hours

Servings: 16

Ingredients:

- 2 cinnamon sticks, each about 3 inches long
- 6-ounce of cherry gelatin
- 4 quarts of apple cider

Directions:

1. Using a 6-quarts slow cooker, pour the apple cider and add the cinnamon stick.
2. Stir, then cover the slow cooker with its lid. Plug in the cooker and let it cook for 3 hours at the high heat setting or until it is heated thoroughly.
3. Then add and stir the gelatin properly, then continue cooking for another hour.
4. When done, remove the cinnamon sticks and serve the drink hot or cold.

Nutrition:

Calories 78

Carbs: 13.2g

Protein: 2.8g

Fat: 1.5g

Fragrant Spiced Coffee

Preparation Time: 10 minutes

Cooking Time: 3 hours

Servings: 8

Ingredients:

4 cinnamon sticks, each about 3 inches long

1 1/2 teaspoons of whole cloves

1/3 cup of honey

2-ounce of chocolate syrup

1/2 teaspoon of anise extract

8 cups of brewed coffee

Directions:

Pour the coffee in a 4-quarts slow cooker and pour in the remaining ingredients except for cinnamon and stir properly.

Wrap the whole cloves in cheesecloth and tie its corners with strings.

Immerse this cheesecloth bag in the liquid present in the slow cooker and cover it with the lid.

Then plug in the slow cooker and let it cook on the low heat setting for 3 hours or until heated thoroughly.

When done, discard the cheesecloth bag and serve.

Nutrition:

Calories 136

Fat 12.6 g

Carbohydrates 4.1 g

Sugar 0.5 g

Protein 10.3 g

Cholesterol 88 mg

Vitamin Green Smoothie

Preparation Time: 5 minutes

Cooking Time: 5 minutes

Servings: 2

Ingredients:

    1 cup milk or juice

    1 cup spinach or kale

½ cup plain yoghurt

1 kiwi

1 Tbsp chia or flax

1 tsp vanilla

Directions:

Mix the milk or juice and greens until smooth. Add
the remaining ingredients and continue blending
until smooth again.

Enjoy your delicious drink!

Nutrition:

Calories 397

Fat 36.4 g

Carbohydrates 4 g

Sugar 1 g

Protein 14.7 g

Cholesterol 4 mg

Inspirational Orange Smoothie

Preparation Time: 5 minutes

Cooking Time: 5 minutes

Servings: 1

Ingredients:

   4 mandarin oranges, peeled

1 banana, sliced and frozen

½ cup non-Fat Greek yoghurt

¼ cup coconut water

1 tsp vanilla extract

5 ice cubes

Directions:

Using a mixer, whisk all the ingredients.
Enjoy your drink!

Nutrition:

Calories 256

Fat 13.3 g

Carbohydrates 0 g

Sugar 0 g

Protein 34.5 g

Cholesterol 78 mg

High Protein Blueberry Banana Smoothie

Preparation Time: 5 minutes

Cooking Time: 5 minutes

Servings: 2

Ingredients:

- 1 cup blueberries, frozen
- 2 ripe bananas
- 1 cup water
- 1 tsp vanilla extract
- 2 Tbsp chia seeds

½ cup cottage cheese

1 tsp lemon zest

Directions:

Put all the smoothie ingredients into the blender
and whisk until smooth.
Enjoy your wonderful smoothie!

Nutrition:

Calories 358

Fat 19.8 g

Carbohydrates 1.3 g

Sugar 0.4 g

Protein 41.9 g

Cholesterol 131 mg

Ginger Smoothie with Citrus and Mint

Preparation Time: 5 minutes

Cooking Time: 3 minutes

Servings: 3

Ingredients:

1 head Romaine lettuce, chopped into 4 chunks

2 Tbsp hemp seeds

5 mandarin oranges, peeled

1 banana, frozen

1 carrot

2-3 mint leaves

½ piece ginger root, peeled

1 cup water

¼ lemon, peeled

½ cup ice

Directions:

Put all the smoothie ingredients in a blender and
blend until smooth.

Enjoy!

Nutrition:

Calories 101

Fat 4 g

Carbohydrates 14 g

Sugar 1 g

Protein 2 g

Cholesterol 3 mg

Strawberry Beet Smoothie

Preparation Time: 5 minutes

Cooking Time: 50 minutes

Servings: 2

Ingredients:

1 red beet, trimmed, peeled and chopped into
   cubes

1 cup strawberries, quartered

1 ripe banana

½ cup strawberry yoghurt

1 Tbsp honey

1 Tbsp water

Directions:

Sprinkle the beet cubes with water, place on
   aluminum foil and put in the oven (preheated to
   204°C). Bake for 40 minutes.

Let the baked beet cool.

Combine all the smoothie ingredients.

Enjoy your fantastic drink.

Nutrition:

Calories 184

Fat 9.2 g

Carbohydrates 1 g

Sugar 0.4 g

Protein 24.9 g

Cholesterol 132 mg

Peanut Butter Shake

Preparation Time: 5 minutes

Cooking Time: 5 minutes

Servings: 2

Ingredients:

1 cup plant-based milk

1 handful kale

2 bananas, frozen

2 Tbsp peanut butter

½ tsp ground cinnamon

¼ tsp vanilla powder

Directions:

Use a blender to combine all the ingredients for
your shake.

Enjoy it!

Nutrition:

Calories 184

Fat 9.2 g

Carbohydrates 1 g

Sugar 0.4 g

Protein 24.9 g

Cholesterol 132 mg

Desserts

Apple Crumble

Preparation Time: 20 minutes

Cooking Time: 25 minutes

Servings: 6

Ingredients:

For the filling

- 4 to 5 apples, cored and chopped (about 6 cups)
- ½ cup unsweetened applesauce, or ¼ cup water
- 2 to 3 tablespoons unrefined sugar (coconut, date, sucanat, maple syrup)
- 1 teaspoon ground cinnamon
- Pinch sea salt

For the crumble

- 2 tablespoons almond butter, or cashew or sunflower seed butter
- 2 tablespoons maple syrup
- 1½ cups rolled oats
- ½ cup walnuts, finely chopped

- ½ teaspoon ground cinnamon
- 2 to 3 tablespoons unrefined granular sugar (coconut, date, sucanat)

Directions:

1. Preparing the Ingredients.
2. Preheat the oven to 350°F. Put the apples and applesauce in an 8-inch-square baking dish, and sprinkle with the sugar, cinnamon, and salt. Toss to combine.
3. In a medium bowl, mix together the nut butter and maple syrup until smooth and creamy. Add the oats, walnuts, cinnamon, and sugar and stir to coat, using your hands if necessary. (If you have a small food processor, pulse the oats and walnuts together before adding them to the mix.)
4. Sprinkle the topping over the apples, and put the dish in the oven.
5. Bake for 20 to 25 minutes, or until the fruit is soft and the topping is lightly browned.

Nutrition:

Calories 195, Fat 7 g, Carbohydrates 6 g, Sugar 2 g, Protein 24 g, Cholesterol 65 mg

Cashew-Chocolate Truffles

Preparation Time: 15 minutes

Cooking Time: 0 minutes

Servings: 12

Ingredients:

- 1 cup raw cashews, soaked in water overnight
- ¾ cup pitted dates
- 2 tablespoons coconut oil
- 1 cup unsweetened shredded coconut, divided
- 1 to 2 tablespoons cocoa powder, to taste

Directions:

Preparing the Ingredients.

1. In a food processor, combine the cashews, dates, coconut oil, ½ cup of shredded coconut, and cocoa powder. Pulse until fully incorporated; it will resemble chunky cookie dough. Spread the remaining ½ cup of shredded coconut on a plate.

2. Form the mixture into tablespoon-size balls and roll on the plate to cover with the

shredded coconut. Transfer to a parchment paper–lined plate or baking sheet. Repeat to make 12 truffles.

3. Place the truffles in the refrigerator for 1 hour to set. Transfer the truffles to a storage container or freezer-safe bag and seal.

Nutrition:

Calories 160

Fat 1 g

Carbohydrates 1 g

Sugar 0.5 g

Protein 22 g

Cholesterol 60 mg

Banana Chocolate Cupcakes

Preparation Time: 20 minutes

Cooking Time: 20 minutes

Servings: 1

Ingredients:

3 medium bananas

1 cup non-dairy milk

2 tablespoons almond butter

1 teaspoon apple cider vinegar

1 teaspoon pure vanilla extract

1¼ cups whole-grain flour

½ cup rolled oats

¼ cup coconut sugar (optional)

1 teaspoon baking powder

½ teaspoon baking soda

½ cup unsweetened cocoa powder

¼ cup chia seeds, or sesame seeds

Pinch sea salt

¼ cup dark chocolate chips, dried cranberries, or
raisins (optional)

Directions:

Preparing the Ingredients.

Preheat the oven to 350°F. Lightly grease the cups of two 6-cup muffin tins or line with paper muffin cups.

Put the bananas, milk, almond butter, vinegar, and vanilla in a blender and purée until smooth. Or stir together in a large bowl until smooth and creamy.

Put the flour, oats, sugar (if using), baking powder, baking soda, cocoa powder, chia seeds, salt, and chocolate chips in another large bowl, and stir to combine. Mix together the wet and dry ingredients, stirring as little as possible. Spoon into muffin cups, and bake for 20 to 25 minutes. Take the cupcakes out of the oven and let them cool fully before taking out of the muffin tins, since they'll be very moist.

Nutrition:

Calories 295

Fat 17 g

Carbohydrates 4 g

Sugar 0.1 g

Protein 29 g

Cholesterol 260 mg

Minty Fruit Salad

Preparation Time: 15 minutes

Cooking Time: 5 minutes

Servings: 4

Ingredients:

   ¼ cup lemon juice (about 2 small lemons)

   4 teaspoons maple syrup or agave syrup

   2 cups chopped pineapple

   2 cups chopped strawberries

   2 cups raspberries

   1 cup blueberries

   8 fresh mint leaves

Directions:

Preparing the Ingredients.

   Beginning with 1 mason jar, add the ingredients in
      this order:

   1 tablespoon of lemon juice, 1 teaspoon of maple
      syrup, ½ cup of pineapple, ½ cup of
      strawberries, ½ cup of raspberries, ¼ cup of
      blueberries, and 2 mint leaves.

   Repeat to fill 3 more jars. Close the jars tightly with
      lids.

Place the airtight jars in the refrigerator for up to 3 days.

Nutrition:

Calories 339

Fat 17.5 g

Carbohydrates 2 g

Sugar 2 g

Protein 44 g

Cholesterol 100 mg

Mango Coconut Cream Pie

Preparation Time: 20 minutes

Cooking Time: 30 minutes

Servings: 8

Ingredients:

For the crust

½ cup rolled oats

1 cup cashews

1 cup soft pitted dates

For the filling

1 cup canned coconut milk

½ cup water

2 large mangos, peeled and chopped, or about 2
cups frozen chunks

½ cup unsweetened shredded coconut

Directions:

Preparing the Ingredients.

Put all the crust ingredients in a food processor and
pulse until it holds together. If you don't have a
food processor, chop everything as finely as
possible and use ½ cup cashew or almond butter
in place of half the cashews. Press the mixture

---

down firmly into an 8-inch pie or springform pan.

Put the all filling ingredients in a blender and purée until smooth (about 1 minute). It should be very thick, so you may have to stop and stir until it's smooth.

Pour the filling into the crust, use a rubber spatula to smooth the top, and put the pie in the freezer until set, about 30 minutes. Once frozen, it should be set out for about 15 minutes to soften before serving.

Top with a batch of Coconut Whipped Cream scooped on top of the pie once it's set. Finish it off with a sprinkling of toasted shredded coconut.

Nutrition:

Calories 545

Fat 39.6 g

Carbohydrates 9.5 g

Sugar 3.1 g

Protein 43 g

Cholesterol 110 mg

Cherry-Vanilla Rice Pudding (Pressure cooker)

Preparation Time: 5 minutes

Cooking Time: 30 minutes

Servings: 4-6

Ingredients:

  1 cup short-grain brown rice

  1¾ cups nondairy milk, plus more as needed

  1½ cups water

  4 tablespoons unrefined sugar or pure maple syrup
  (use 2 tablespoons if you use a sweetened milk),
  plus more as needed

  1 teaspoon vanilla extract (use ½ teaspoon if you
  use vanilla milk)

  Pinch salt

  ¼ cup dried cherries or ½ cup fresh or frozen pitted
  cherries

Directions:

  Preparing the Ingredients. In your electric pressure
  cooker's cooking pot, combine the rice, milk,
  water, sugar, vanilla, and salt.

High pressure for 30 minutes. Close and lock the lid, and select High Pressure for 30 minutes.

Pressure Release. Once the **Cooking Time:** is complete, let the pressure release naturally, about 20 minutes. Unlock and remove the lid. Stir in the cherries and put the lid back on loosely for about 10 minutes. Serve, adding more milk or sugar, as desired.

Nutrition:

Calories 420

Fat 27.4 g

Carbohydrates 2 g

Sugar 0.3 g

Protein 46.3 g

Cholesterol 98 mg

Lime in the Coconut Chia Pudding

Preparation Time: 10 minutes

Cooking Time: 20 minutes

Servings: 4

Ingredients:

Zest and juice of 1 lime

1 (14-ounce) can coconut milk

1 to 2 dates, or 1 tablespoon coconut or other
unrefined sugar, or 1 tablespoon maple syrup, or
10 to 15 drops pure liquid stevia

2 tablespoons chia seeds, whole or ground

2 teaspoons matcha green tea powder (optional)

Directions:

Preparing the Ingredients.

Blend all the ingredients in a blender until smooth.
Chill in the fridge for about 20 minutes, then
serve topped with one or more of the topping
ideas.

Try blueberries, blackberries, sliced strawberries,
Coconut Whipped Cream, or toasted
unsweetened coconut.

Nutrition:

Calories 381

Fat 17.1 g

Carbohydrates 4.1 g

Sugar 0.6 g

Protein 50.6 g

Cholesterol 358 mg

Mint Chocolate Chip Sorbet

Preparation Time: 5 minutes

Cooking Time: 0 minute

Servings: 1

Ingredients:

1 frozen banana

1 tablespoon almond butter, or peanut butter, or
other nut or seed butter

2 tablespoons fresh mint, minced

¼ cup or less non-dairy milk (only if needed)

2 to 3 tablespoons non-dairy chocolate chips, or
cocoa nibs

2 to 3 tablespoons goji berries (optional)

Directions:

Preparing the Ingredients.

Put the banana, almond butter, and mint in a food
processor or blender and purée until smooth.

Add the non-dairy milk if needed to keep blending
(but only if needed, as this will make the texture
less solid). Pulse the chocolate chips and goji
berries (if using) into the mix so they're roughly
chopped up.

Nutrition:

Calories 299

Fat 16 g

Carbohydrates 3 g

Sugar 6 g

Protein 38 g

Cholesterol 108 mg

Peach-Mango Crumble (Pressure cooker)

Preparation Time: 10 minutes

Cooking Time: 6 minutes

Servings: 4-6

Ingredient:

- 3 cups chopped fresh or frozen peaches
- 3 cups chopped fresh or frozen mangos
- 4 tablespoons unrefined sugar or pure maple syrup, divided
- 1 cup gluten-free rolled oats
- ½ cup shredded coconut, sweetened or unsweetened
- 2 tablespoons coconut oil or vegan margarine

Directions:

Preparing the Ingredients. In a 6- to 7-inch round baking dish, toss together the peaches, mangos, and 2 tablespoons of sugar. In a food processor, combine the oats, coconut, coconut oil, and remaining 2 tablespoons of sugar. Pulse until combined. (If you use maple syrup, you'll need less coconut oil. Start with just the syrup and add oil if the mixture isn't sticking together.) Sprinkle the oat mixture over the fruit mixture.

Cover the dish with aluminum foil. Put a trivet in the bottom of your electric pressure cooker's cooking pot and pour in a cup or two of water. Using a foil sling or silicone helper handles, lower the pan onto the trivet.

High pressure for 6 minutes. Close and lock the lid, and select High Pressure for 6 minutes.

Pressure Release. Once the **Cooking Time:** is complete, quick release the pressure. Unlock and remove the lid.

Let cool for a few minutes before carefully lifting out the dish with oven mitts or tongs. Scoop out portions to serve.

Nutrition:

Calories 275

Fat 19 g

Carbohydrates 19 g

Sugar 4 g

Protein 14 g

Cholesterol 60 mg

Zesty Orange-Cranberry Energy Bites

Preparation Time: 10 minutes

Cooking Time: 15 minutes

Servings: 12

Ingredients:

2 tablespoons almond butter, or cashew or
    sunflower seed butter

2 tablespoons maple syrup, or brown rice syrup

¾ cup cooked quinoa

¼ cup sesame seeds, toasted

1 tablespoon chia seeds

½ teaspoon almond extract, or vanilla extract

Zest of 1 orange

1 tablespoon dried cranberries

¼ cup ground almonds

Directions:

Preparing the Ingredients.

In a medium bowl, mix together the nut or seed
    butter and syrup until smooth and creamy. Stir
    in the rest of the ingredients, and mix to make

---

sure the consistency is holding together in a ball. Form the mix into 12 balls.

Place them on a baking sheet lined with parchment or waxed paper and put in the fridge to set for about 15 minutes.

If your balls aren't holding together, it's likely because of the moisture content of your cooked quinoa. Add more nut or seed butter mixed with syrup until it all sticks together.

Nutrition:

Calories 493

Fat 33 g

Carbohydrates 8 g

Sugar 9 g

Protein 47 g

Cholesterol 135 mg

Almond-Date Energy Bites

Preparation Time: 5 minutes

Cooking Time: 15 minutes

Servings: 24

Ingredients:

1 cup dates, pitted

1 cup unsweetened shredded coconut

¼ cup chia seeds

¾ cup ground almonds

¼ cup cocoa nibs, or non-dairy chocolate chips

Directions:

Purée everything in a food processor until crumbly and sticking together, pushing down the sides whenever necessary to keep it blending. If you don't have a food processor, you can mash soft Medjool dates. But if you're using harder baking dates, you'll have to soak them and then try to purée them in a blender.

Form the mix into 24 balls and place them on a baking sheet lined with parchment or waxed paper. Put in the fridge to set for about 15 minutes. Use the softest dates you can find.

Medjool dates are the best for this purpose. The hard dates you see in the baking aisle of your supermarket are going to take a long time to blend up. If you use those, try soaking them in water for at least an hour before you start, and then draining.

Nutrition:

Calories 171

Fat 4 g

Carbohydrates 7 g

Sugar 7 g

Protein 22 g

Cholesterol 65 mg

Pumpkin Pie Cups (Pressure cooker)

Preparation Time: 5 minutes

Cooking Time: 6 minutes

Servings: 4-6

Ingredients:

  1 cup canned pumpkin purée

  1 cup nondairy milk

  6 tablespoons unrefined sugar or pure maple syrup (less if using sweetened milk), plus more for sprinkling

  ¼ cup spelt flour or whole-grain flour

  ½ teaspoon pumpkin pie spice

  Pinch salt

Directions:

  Preparing the Ingredients. In a medium bowl, stir together the pumpkin, milk, sugar, flour, pumpkin pie spice, and salt. Pour the mixture into 4 heat-proof ramekins. Sprinkle a bit more sugar on the top of each, if you like. Put a trivet in the bottom of your electric pressure cooker's cooking pot and pour in a cup or two of water. Place the ramekins onto the trivet, stacking them if needed (3 on the bottom, 1 on top).

High pressure for 6 minutes. Close and lock the lid, and select High Pressure for 6 minutes.

Pressure Release. Once the **Cooking Time:** is complete, quick release the pressure. Unlock and remove the lid. Let cool for a few minutes before carefully lifting out the ramekins with oven mitts or tongs. Let cool for at least 10 minutes before serving.

Nutrition:

Calories 152

Fat 4 g

Carbohydrates 4 g

Sugar 8 g

Protein 18 g

Cholesterol 51 mg

Fudgy Brownies (Pressure cooker)

Preparation Time: 10 minutes

Cooking Time: 5 minutes

Servings: 4-6

Ingredients:

3 ounces dairy-free dark chocolate

1 tablespoon coconut oil or vegan margarine

½ cup applesauce

2 tablespoons unrefined sugar

1/3 cup whole-grain flour

½ teaspoon baking powder

Pinch salt

Directions:

Preparing the Ingredients. Put a trivet in your electric pressure cooker's cooking pot and pour in a cup or two of two of water. Select Sauté or Simmer. In a large heat-proof glass or ceramic bowl, combine the chocolate and coconut oil. Place the bowl over the top of your pressure cooker, as you would a double boiler. Stir occasionally until the chocolate is melted, then turn off the pressure cooker. Stir the applesauce and sugar into the chocolate mixture. Add the flour, baking powder, and salt and stir just until combined. Pour the batter into 3 heat-proof ramekins. Put them in a heat-proof dish and cover with aluminum foil. Using a foil sling or silicone helper handles, lower the dish onto the trivet. (Alternately, cover each ramekin with foil and place them directly on the trivet, without the dish.)

High pressure for 6 minutes. Close and lock the lid, and select High Pressure for 5 minutes.

Pressure Release. Once the **Cooking Time:** is complete, quick release the pressure. Unlock and remove the lid.

Let cool for a few minutes before carefully lifting out the dish, or ramekins, with oven mitts or tongs. Let cool for a few minutes more before serving.

Top with fresh raspberries and an extra drizzle of melted chocolate.

Nutrition:

Calories 256

Fat 29 g

Carbohydrates 1 g

Sugar 0.5 g

Protein 11 g

Cholesterol 84 mg

Coconut-Banana Pudding

Preparation Time: 4 minutes

Cooking Time: 5 minutes

Servings: 4

Ingredients:

   3 bananas, divided

   1 (13.5-ounce) can full-Fat coconut milk

   ¼ cup organic cane sugar

   1 tablespoon cornstarch

   1 teaspoon vanilla extract

   2 pinches sea salt

   6 drops natural yellow food coloring (optional)

   Ground cinnamon, for garnish

Directions:

Preparing the Ingredients.

Combine 1 banana, the coconut milk, sugar,
   cornstarch, vanilla, and salt in a blender. Blend
   until smooth and creamy. If you're using the
   food coloring, add it to the blender now and
   blend until the color is evenly dispersed.

Transfer to a saucepot and bring to a boil over
   medium-high heat. Immediately reduce to a

simmer and whisk for 3 minutes, or until the mixture thickens to a thin pudding and sticks to a spoon.

Transfer the mixture to a container and allow to cool for 1 hour. Cover and refrigerate overnight to set. When you're ready to serve, slice the remaining 2 bananas and build individual servings as follows: pudding, banana slices, pudding, and so on until a single-serving dish is filled to the desired level. Sprinkle with ground cinnamon.

Nutrition:

Calories 170

Fat 4 g

Carbohydrates 34 g

Sugar 14g

Protein 9 g

Cholesterol 14 mg

Spiced Apple Chia Pudding

Preparation Time: 5 minutes

Cooking Time: 0 minutes

Servings: 1

Ingredients:

½ cup unsweetened applesauce

¼ cup nondairy milk or canned coconut milk

1 tablespoon chia seeds

1½ teaspoons sugar

Pinch ground cinnamon or pumpkin pie spice

Directions:

Preparing the Ingredients.

In a small bowl, stir together the applesauce, milk, chia seeds, sugar, and cinnamon. Enjoy as is, or let sit for 30 minutes so the chia seeds soften and expand.

Nutrition:

Calories 145,Fat 4 g,Carbohydrates 19 g,Sugar 9 g Protein 2 g,Cholesterol 26 mg

Salted Coconut-Almond Fudge

Preparation Time: 5 minutes

Cooking Time: 0 minutes

Servings: 12

Ingredients:

¾ cup creamy almond butter

½ cup maple syrup

1/3 cup coconut oil, softened or melted

6 tablespoons fair-trade unsweetened cocoa powder

1 teaspoon coarse or flaked sea salt

Directions:

Preparing the Ingredients.

Line a loaf pan with a double layer of plastic wrap. Place one layer horizontally in the pan with a generous amount of overhang, and the second layer vertically with a generous amount of overhang.

In a medium bowl, gently mix together the almond butter, maple syrup, and coconut oil until well combined and smooth. Add the cocoa powder and gently stir it into the mixture until well combined and creamy.

Pour the mixture into the prepared pan and sprinkle with the sea salt. Bring the overflowing edges of the plastic wrap over the top of the fudge to completely cover it. Place the pan in the freezer for at least 1 hour or overnight, until the fudge is firm.

Remove the pan from the freezer and lift the fudge out of the pan using the plastic-wrap overhangs to pull it out. Transfer to a cutting board and cut into 1-inch pieces.

Nutrition:

Calories 297

Fat 20.3 g

Carbohydrates 4 g

Sugar 5 g

Protein 21 g

Cholesterol 80 mg

Caramelized Bananas

Preparation Time: 5 minutes

Cooking Time: 10 minutes

Servings: 2

Ingredients:

  2 tablespoons vegan margarine or coconut oil

  2 bananas, peeled, halved crosswise and then
    lengthwise

  2 tablespoons dark brown sugar, demerara sugar,
    or coconut sugar

  2 tablespoons spiced apple cider

  Chopped walnuts, for topping

Directions:

Preparing the Ingredients.

Melt the margarine in a nonstick skillet over
    medium heat. Add the bananas, and cook for 2
    minutes. Flip, and cook for 2 minutes more.

Sprinkle the sugar and cider into the oil around the
    bananas, and cook for 2 to 3 minutes, until the
    sauce thickens and caramelizes around the
    bananas. Carefully scoop the bananas into small

bowls, and drizzle with any remaining liquid in the skillet. Sprinkle with walnuts.

Nutrition:

Calories: 413

Fat: 13g

Saturated Fat: 4g

Cholesterol: 98mg

Sodium: 432mg

Carbohydrates: 64g

Fiber: 5g

Protein: 37g

"Rugged" Coconut Balls

Preparation Time: 15 minutes

Cooking Time: 0 minute

Servings: 8

Ingredients:

1/3 cup coconut oil melted

1/3 cup coconut butter softened

2 oz coconut, finely shredded, unsweetened

4 Tbsp coconut palm sugar

1/2 cup shredded coconut

Directions:

Combine all ingredients in a blender.

Blend until soft and well combined.

Form small balls from the mixture and roll in
    shredded coconut.

Place on a sheet lined with parchment paper and
refrigerate overnight.

Keep coconut balls into sealed container in fridge up
to one week.

Nutrition:

Calories: 247

Total Fat: 7g

Saturated Fat: 2g

Cholesterol: 17mg

Sodium: 563mg

Carbohydrates: 33g

Fiber: 3g

Protein: 12g

Almond - Choco Cake

Preparation Time: 45 minutes

Cooking Time: 32 minutes

Servings: 8

Ingredients:

1 1/2 cups of almond flour

1/3 cup almonds finely chopped

1/4 cup of cocoa powder unsweetened

Pinch of salt

1/2 tsp baking soda

2 Tbsp almond milk

1/2 cup Coconut oil melted

2 tsp pure vanilla extract

1/3 cup brown sugar (packed)

Directions:

Preheat oven to 350 F.

Line 9" cake pan with parchment paper, and grease with a little melted coconut oil; set aside.

Stir the almond flour, chopped almonds, cocoa powder, salt, and baking soda in a bowl.

In a separate bowl, stir the remaining ingredients.

Combine the almond flour mixture with the almond milk mixture and stir well.

Place batter in a prepared cake pan.

Bake for 30 to 32 minutes.

Remove from the oven, allow it to cool completely.

Store the cake-slices a freezer, tightly wrapped in a double layer of plastic wrap and a layer of foil. It will keep on this way for up to a month.

Nutrition:

Calories: 460

Total Fat: 32g

Saturated Fat: 23g

Cholesterol: 223mg

Sodium: 902mg

Carbohydrates: 16g

Fiber: 5g

Protein: 29g

Banana-Almond Cake

Preparation Time: 15 minutes

Cooking Time: 45 minutes

Servings: 8

Ingredients:

4 ripe bananas in chunks

3 Tbsš honey or maple syrup

1 tsp pure vanilla extract

1/2 cup almond milk

3/4 cup of self-rising flour

1 tsp cinnamon

1 tsp baking powder

1 pinch of salt

1/3 cup of almonds finely chopped

Almond slices for decoration

Directions:

Preheat the oven to 400 F (air mode).

Oil a cake mold; set aside.

Add bananas into a bowl and mash with the fork.

Add honey, vanilla, almond, and stir well.

In a separate bowl, stir flour, cinnamon, baking powder, salt, the almonds broken, and mix with a spoon.

Combine the flour mixture with the banana mixture, and stir until all ingredients combined well.

Transfer the mixture to prepared cake mold and sprinkle with sliced almonds.

Bake for 40-45 minutes or until the toothpick inserted comes out clean.

Remove from the oven, and allow the cake to cool completely.

Cut cake into slices, place in tin foil, or an airtight container, and keep refrigerated up to one week.

Nutrition:

Calories: 301,Total Fat: 8g,Saturated Fat: 1g

Cholesterol: 99mg,Sodium: 08mg,

Carbohydrates: 21g,Fiber: 4g,Protein: 26g

Banana-Coconut Ice Cream

Preparation Time: 15 minutes

Cooking Time: 0 minutes

Servings: 6

Ingredients:

1 cup coconut cream

1/2 cup Inverted sugar

2 large frozen bananas (chunks)

3 Tbsp honey extracted

1/4 tsp cinnamon powder

Directions:

In a bowl, whip the coconut cream with the inverted
sugar.

In a separate bowl, beat the banana with honey and
cinnamon.

Incorporate the coconut whipped cream and banana
   mixture; stir well.

Cover the bowl and let cool in the refrigerator over
   the night.

Stir the mixture 3 to 4 times to avoid crystallization.

Keep frozen 1 to 2 months.

Nutrition:

Calories: 257

Total Fat: 4g

Saturated Fat: 0g

Cholesterol: 33mg

Sodium: 819mg

Carbohydrates: 37g

Fiber: 7g

Protein: 20g

Coconut Butter Clouds Cookies

Preparation Time: 15 minutes

Cooking Time: 10 minutes

Servings: 8

Ingredients:

1/2 cup coconut butter softened

1/2 cup peanut butter softened

1/2 cup of granulated sugar

1/2 cup of brown sugar

2 Tbsp chia seeds soaked in 4 tablespoons water

1/2 tsp pure vanilla extract

1/2 tsp baking soda

1/4 tsp salt

1 cup of all-purpose flour

Directions:

Preheat oven to 360 F.

Add coconut butter, peanut butter, and both sugars
in a mixing bowl.

Beat with a mixer until soft and sugar combined
well.

Add soaked chia seeds and vanilla extract; beat.

Add baking soda, salt, and flour; beat until all
ingredients are combined well.

With your hands, shape dough into cookies.

Arrange your cookies onto a baking sheet, and bake
for about 10 minutes.

Remove cookies from the oven and allow to cool
completely.

Sprinkle with icing sugar and enjoy your cookies.

Place cookies in an airtight container and keep
refrigerated up to 10 days.

Nutrition:

Calories: 731

Total Fat: 26g

Saturated Fat: 17g

Cholesterol: 169mg

Sodium: 1167mg

Carbohydrates: 56g

Fiber: 5g,Protein: 45g

Chocomint Hazelnut Bars

Preparation Time: 5 minutes

Cooking Time: 15 minutes

Servings: 8

Ingredients:

1/2 cup coconut oil, melted

4 Tbsp cocoa powder

1/4 cup almond butter

3/4 cup brown sugar - (packed)

1 tsp vanilla extract

1 tsp pure peppermint extract

pinch of salt

1 cup shredded coconut

1 cup hazelnuts sliced

Directions:

Chop the hazelnuts in a food processor; set aside.

Fill the bottom of a double boiler with water and place it on low heat.

Put the coconut oil, cacao powder, almond butter, brown sugar, vanilla, peppermint extract, and salt in the top of a double boiler over hot (not boiling) water and constantly stir for 10 minutes.

Add hazelnuts and shredded coconut to the melted mixture and stir together.

Pour the mixture in a dish lined with parchment and freeze for several hours.

Remove from the freezer and cut into bars.

Store in airtight container or freezer bag in a freezer.

Let the bars at room temperature for 10 to 15 minutes before eating.

Nutrition:

Calories: 186

Total Fat: 4g

Saturated Fat: 0g

Cholesterol: 33mg

Sodium: 783mg

Carbohydrates: 23g

Fiber: 6g,Protein: 19g

Coco-Cinnamon Balls

Preparation Time: 10 minutes

Cooking Time: 5 minutes

Servings: 12

Ingredients:

1 cup coconut butter softened

1 cup coconut milk canned

1 tsp pure vanilla extract

3/4 tsp cinnamon

1/2 tsp nutmeg

2 Tbsp coconut palm sugar (or granulated sugar)

1 cup coconut shreds

Directions:

Combine all ingredients (except the coconut shreds)
in a heated bath - bain-marie.

Cook and stir until all ingredients are soft and well combined.

Remove bowl from heat, place into a bowl, and refrigerate until the mixture firmed up.

Form cold coconut mixture into balls, and roll each ball in the shredded coconut.

Store into a sealed container, and keep refrigerated up to one week.

Nutrition:

Calories: 213

Fat: 6g

Fiber: 13g

Carbs: 16g

Protein: 22g

Chocolate and Avocado Pudding

Preparation Time: 3 hours and 10 minutes

Cooking Time: 0 minute

Servings: 1

Ingredients:

- 1 small avocado, pitted, peeled
- 1 small banana, mashed
- 1/3 cup cocoa powder, unsweetened
- 1 tablespoon cacao nibs, unsweetened
- 1/4 cup maple syrup
- 1/3 cup coconut cream

Directions:

1. Add avocado in a food processor along with cream and then pulse for 2 minutes until smooth.
2. Add remaining ingredients, blend until mixed, and then tip the pudding in a container.
3. Cover the container with a plastic wrap; it should touch the pudding and refrigerate for 3 hours.
4. Serve straight away.

Nutrition:

Calories: 87 Cal

Fat: 7 g

Carbs: 9 g

Protein: 1.5 g

Fiber: 3.2 g

Conclusion

In a nutshell, this cookbook offers you a world full of options to diversify your plant-based menu. People on this diet are usually seen struggling to choose between healthy food and flavor but, soon, they run out of the options. The selection of 250 recipes in this book is enough to adorn your dinner table with flavorsome, plant-based meals every day. Give each recipe a good read and try them out in the kitchen. You will experience tempting aromas and binding flavors every day.

The book is conceptualized with the idea of offering you a comprehensive view of a plant-based diet and how it can benefit the body. You may find the shift sudden, especially if you are a die-hard fan of non-vegetarian items. But you need not give up anything that you love. Eat everything in moderation.

The next step is to start experimenting with the different recipes in this book and see which ones are your favorites. Everyone has their favorite food, and you will surely find several of yours in this book. Start with breakfast and work your way through. You will be pleasantly surprised at how tasty a vegan meal really can be.

You will love reading this book, as it helps you to understand how revolutionary a plant-based diet can be. It will help you to make informed decisions as you move toward greater change for the greater good. What are you waiting for? Have you begun your journey on the path of the plant-based diet yet? If you haven't, do it now! Now you have everything you need to get started making budget-friendly, healthy plant-based recipes. Just follow your basic shopping list and follow your meal plan to get started! It's easy to switch over to a plant-based diet if you have your meals planned out and temptation locked away. Don't forget to clean out your kitchen before starting, and you're sure to meet all your diet and health goals.

You need to plan if you are thinking about dieting. First, you can start slowly by just eating one meal a day, which is vegetarian and gradually increasing your number of vegetarian meals. Whenever you are struggling, ask your friend or family member to support you and keep you motivated. One important thing is also to be regularly accountable for not following the diet.

If dieting seems very important to you and you need to do it right, then it is recommended that you visit a professional such as a nutritionist or dietitian to discuss your dieting plan and optimizing it for the better.

No matter how much you want to lose weight, it is not advised that you decrease your calorie intake to an unhealthy level. Losing weight does not mean that you stop eating. It is done by carefully planning meals.

A plant-based diet is very easy once you get into it. At first, you will start to face a lot of difficulties, but if you start slowly, then you can face all the barriers and achieve your goal.

Swap out one unhealthy food item each week that you know is not helping you and put in its place one of the plant-based ingredients that you like. Then have some fun creating the many different recipes in this book. Find out what recipes you like the most so you can make them often and most of all; have some fun exploring all your recipe options.

Wish you good luck with the plant-based diet!

CPSIA information can be obtained
at www.ICGtesting.com
Printed in the USA
BVHW040932120421
604730BV00016B/378

9 781801 834704